D1480685

THE NAVAJO

Also by the same author

THE APACHE INDIANS
Raiders of the Southwest
THE AZTEC
Indians of Mexico
THE CHEROKEE
Indians of the Mountains
THE CHIPPEWA INDIANS
Rice Gatherers of the Great Lakes
THE CROW INDIANS
Hunters of the Northern Plains
THE DELAWARE INDIANS
Eastern Fishermen and Farmers
THE ESKIMO
Arctic Hunters and Trappers
HORSEMEN OF THE WESTERN PLATEAUS
The Nez Percé Indians
THE INCA
Indians of the Andes
INDIANS OF THE LONGHOUSE
The Story of the Iroquois
THE MAYA
Indians of Central America
THE MISSION INDIANS OF CALIFORNIA
THE NAVAJO
Herders, Weavers, and Silversmiths
THE PUEBLO INDIANS
Farmers of the Rio Grande
THE SEA HUNTERS
Indians of the Northwest Coast
THE SEMINOLE INDIANS
THE SIOUX INDIANS
Hunters and Warriors of the Plains

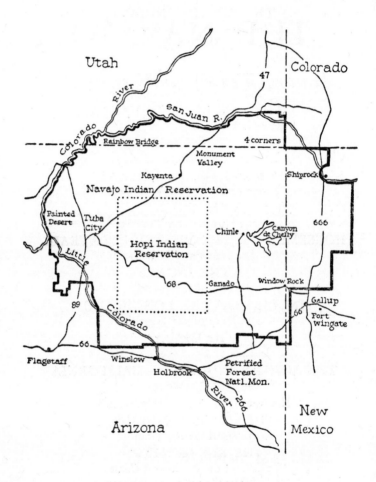

THE NAVAJO

Herders, Weavers, and Silversmiths

BY SONIA BLEEKER

Illustrated by Patricia Boodell

WILLIAM MORROW AND COMPANY

NEW YORK • 1958

HARDEMAN COUNTY LIBRARY
QUANAH, TEXAS

© 1958 by Sonia Bleeker
All rights reserved.
Published simultaneously in the Dominion of
Canada by George J. McLeod Limited, Toronto.
Printed in the United States of America.

Thirteenth Printing, October 1974

Library of Congress Catalog Card No. 58-5025

Grateful recognition is given to
Mr. Stanley A. Stubbs
Museum of New Mexico, Sante Fe, New Mexico,
for reading and criticizing the manuscript.

CONTENTS

I

THE NEW HOGAN

"You'll be running with closed eyes," Mother teased Slim Runner. "Wake up. The sun will be up before you."

Slim Runner seemed to be asleep, breathing evenly under his sheepskin. Actually, he was just keeping his eyes shut as he snuggled under the warm cover. Like all Navajo (Nahv'-ah-ho), he enjoyed a good joke. Mother reached for his foot under the sheepskin and began to tickle it. Slim Runner held his breath, so that he would not burst out laughing and give himself away.

"We should have called him Lazy Boy," Father said. He tied his red kerchief about his head, to keep his long hair in place, and sat down on the clean-swept earth floor to sip his

11

morning coffee. Mother warmed corncakes on an iron griddle in the firepit. She handed a hot cake to Father and set two bowls in the children's places.

Sister, as usual, came to Slim Runner's rescue. Even though he was thirteen, she always defended him, as if he were a small child. "Are you running out of names?" she asked Father. "You used to call Older Brother Lazy Boy. Now that he is away at school, you're teasing Younger Brother. He is not lazy. He runs faster than an antelope."

It was still quite dark inside the hogan (hogahn'). Mother was putting on her shawl to go out to the corral to milk the goats.

Slim Runner stirred, and Sister said to him, "Come. I am ready, Younger Brother. We must start before the sun is seen."

"Run by yourself today," Slim Runner retorted, yawning. He stood up and began to dress. "It's cold outside," he said to Mother. "And it's no fun running *behind* Sister day after day." He buttoned his flannel shirt and picked up his boots.

"That's the custom, Son," Mother reminded Slim Runner. "It is right for a girl, when she is growing up, to run each morning toward the rising sun. The spirits will see that she is not lazy, and will reward her with good health, happiness, and beauty. It is proper for her brother to run with her. But he must not outrun her. Anyone who outruns a girl on these morning races may get sick and die."

Mother raised the shawl, so that it covered the back of her head. Then she moved the heavy blanket from the entrance to the hogan and stepped over the high threshold. Slim Runner finished pulling on his boots. "Start ahead," he told Sister. "I'll catch up with you." Sister darted out of the hogan. She ran east, toward the rising sun. Slim Runner soon followed her. Father came out last. He saddled and mounted his horse, and was off for a day's work in the cornfield.

The sun was just rising over the rim of the mesa (may'-sa), the flat-topped hill that stood between the hogan and the valley below. All of a sudden, the sky lit up with gold, and the dark mesa took on an orange glow that deepened into red. Ahead of Slim Runner, Sister's wide skirt now took on its yellow color. The light spilled over her purple velveteen blouse and glossy black braids.

Without effort, Slim Runner loped along behind Sister as they both ran toward the mesa. His heels barely touched the fine red sand. The boy could now see the uneven, eroded columns of red sandstone on the wall of the mesa. Sister fleetingly touched one of the columns and started back, passing Slim Runner with a wave of her hand. He, too, turned back, but kept well behind Sister.

The sheep were bleating in the corral by the hogan. They pressed against the split logs that formed the walls of the corral. Slim Runner ran into the hogan. He crouched down quickly

by the firepit and picked up a warm corncake.
Mother poured the hot coffee into a tin cup.
The boy drank it, scalding his throat. "Hot,"
he said. He blew into the cup, pursing his lips.
Mother wrapped another corncake in a piece
of cloth for his lunch and then poured a cup
of goat's milk from the pail for him. Slim Runner drank it quickly. It cooled his throat, and
he smiled at Mother as he handed the cup back
to her. "I'll take the sheep to that new place,
where I had them yesterday," he said. "Down
in the valley, behind the mesa, there is still a
good flow of water in the wash. And there is
grass. I want to get there before another herder
finds the place."

Mother wrapped her shawl about her again,
picked up a bundle of wool, and followed Slim
Runner out of the hogan. She sat down in front
of her upright loom and started her day's weaving. The large rug she was weaving was almost finished. Soon she would take it to the
trading post and sell it. The money she received

for her rugs would buy groceries for the family.

Sister pulled out the two poles that made up the crude corral gate, and the sheep and goats came tumbling out, crowding and bleating. The sheep dog jumped up and down in front of the herd, bunching them together. Slim Runner threw his worn saddle blanket on his horse and, grabbing the horse's mane, jumped astride him.

There were about twenty-five goats and kids in the herd. The rest were sheep. More than half of them belonged to Mother. The remainder belonged to Older Brother, Sister, and Slim Runner. According to custom, Father's sheep were being herded by his mother's family, who lived toward the southeast of the Navajo Reservation.

To most people, a herd of sheep and long-haired goats are just a mass of animals. To a Navajo sheepherder, each one has an individual face, carriage, and set of markings. Slim Runner knew every animal in the flock. If his herd were to get mixed with another, he would have no difficulty in singling out each of his sheep and goats.

Slim Runner counted the herd from horseback, eyeing each sheep as it crowded past him. The kids and lambs looked plump and sleek. He had been lucky last spring. Very few of them had died at birth. Sheepherders in this overgrazed region expect to lose quite a few young, because too often the dams don't get enough good pasturage. Slim Runner planned to take the herd a bit farther down the wash today. Since sheep and goats are the main source of food, wool and skins, and cash income for most Navajo households, he was anxious to make sure that they were well fed.

Slim Runner reined in his horse in the center of the unpaved, dusty road that led eastward across the plateau from Kayenta (Kay-yen'-tay). Farther south there was a good paved road for

fast automobiles. Dirt roads crisscrossed the vast
Navajo Reservation and were used mainly by
horses, wagons, and pickup trucks.

A pickup truck stopped and waited for the
herd to cross the road. Slim Runner did not
know the Navajo family in the truck. He
thought that they must be returning from either
Kayenta or Tuba City, because they were all
dressed up. The Navajo like to dress up in
their best, with lots of turquoise necklaces,
bracelets, and rings, when they go to town. The
herd crossed the road, and Slim Runner waved
his hand to the driver to thank him for stop-
ping.

It was still quite cool when Slim Runner
reached the pasture. In the distance, another
herd of sheep and goats was grazing. Slim
Runner slid off his horse. The herd spread out,
nibbling at the green grass. He hobbled the
horse and turned him out to graze, too. Slim
Runner sat down on a rock near a bushy juniper
and looked down at the valley below, at the

sandy wash with its trickling, muddy water. The cottonwoods in the distance were turning an autumn gold, but the sagebrush remained the same dull blue-gray color. Farther on toward the horizon, where the cloudless blue sky met the red earth, were cluttered mesas, tall twisted buttes, and forest. This was Navajo country.

The Navajo, the largest tribe of Indians in the United States, now number close to 85,000 people. They occupy some 25,000 square miles of near-desert land in western New Mexico, eastern Arizona, and southern Utah. This region is as big as the states of New Hampshire, Vermont, and Rhode Island combined. The boundaries are four mountains, which are sacred to the Navajo. Their lands are made up of rocky plateaus and canyons cut by wind and water. Cottonwood trees rim the canyons, and poplars and pines grow in the mountain areas. Sagebrush, junipers, and piñon pines cover the land.

The Navajo believe that their ancestors, like the ancestors of many other Indian groups, came up out of the underworld. The gods and spirits helped them to emerge, guided them, and taught them how to keep well and happy on earth. The gods gave them the name Dineh (Dee'-ney), which means "the people." The Navajo call themselves Dineh today, and use the name *Navajo* only when they speak English. This name means "large, cultivated lands." Although many official publications spell Navajo with an "h," the Navajo themselves prefer that it be spelled with a "j."

The Navajo were a rich people about a hundred years ago, when the United States government first assumed control over them. They numbered about one fourth their present population, and owned large flocks of sheep and goats and herds of horses. At that time their lands were still covered with rich grass. Today the area is overgrazed and can barely support the half million sheep and goats that the Navajo

own. The job of the Navajo sheepherders today is to find enough grass for their flocks
within the limits of the reservation. Sheepherders wander up and down the sun-baked
mesas, into the foothills of the mountains, and
down the canyons in search of forage. The
sheep and goats nibble the grasses down to the
roots, then trample on them with their sharp
little hoofs till the roots are killed off. Thus
they turn another piece of grazing land into
desert.

The Navajo families roam about the reservation, following their herds. They move with
the herd to higher areas in spring and summer,
and search for lower, protected areas in fall
and winter. Clusters of hogans all over Navajo
country stand silent and deserted in summer and
early fall. While the people are away from the
hogan, they build shelters of saplings and brush.
Each shelter has a firepit, a few cooking uten-
sils, and a loom. This becomes a temporary
home for the family till the herd eats all the

grass in the neighborhood. The family then moves again. But a family likes to return for the winter to its more substantial home, the hogan. A Navajo always regards the hogan as his real home, no matter how long he has been away from it.

As Slim Runner looked over the wide expanse of plateau and canyons before him, he thought, This would make a beautiful site for the new hogan my family needs. Mother and Father had been talking about building a new hogan. The one they were living in was small and worn, and there wasn't even a good door to keep out the cold. The brush-covered roof stirred with the slightest breeze. The family feared that it would cave in with the first storm.

Slim Runner faced east, imagining himself standing in the doorway of a new hogan. Navajo hogans always face east, toward the rising sun. Slim Runner felt the sun warming him, as though welcoming him to remain right there.

The boy broke a twig from a nearby bush and sharpened one end with his pocketknife. Whenever Slim Runner wanted to visualize anything or to explain to his family something that he had seen, he found it helpful to draw a picture. During the long days with the herd, the boy often amused himself by drawing sheep and goats in the sand. Other sheepherders liked to come over to watch Slim Runner draw.

"Someday you will make a good sand painter," Father had said seriously one day. "Mother and I should take you to more ceremonies, so that you could see how the Navajo sand painters work. You would learn a very good thing, and people from all over would come to you for help."

Looking up at his grazing sheep, Slim Runner first drew a corral for them—a much larger one than they had at present. He made a larger water trough, too. The water trough by the old hogan was dry most of the time. But here the water would be so much nearer, Slim

Runner thought, that he would certainly keep the large trough filled.

Behind the large corral, Slim Runner drew a smaller one. "For Sister's pigs," he said to himself. Mother had bought three pigs that past spring. They would be eaten in the winter, when food was scarce. Mother did not want to kill too many sheep, because she was afraid she would not have enough wool for weaving rugs. The pigs were Sister's special responsibility, and she fed them well. They had grown big and fat, and were able to push the sheep about. Slim Runner thought that it would be more peaceful with two corrals.

Slim Runner now drew a six-sided hogan. We believe that the style for the Navajo hogan of today was suggested to them in the 1880's, when they learned to use discarded railroad ties. It is said among the Navajo that the ceremonial houses the gods had taught them to build were also six-sided. Prior to the 1880's, the Navajo hogans were rounded, earth-covered huts, built on a framework of upright logs.

Slim Runner drew rounded logs and made the overlapping joints even. Instead of a rough, brush-covered roof, he made the domed roof smooth. Uncle (Mother's brother) had built himself a hogan and covered it with tar paper. And it was really rainproof. Uncle's hogan also had two windows, and a real door instead of a blanket. Slim Runner drew a door and a window. He was so pleased with the results that he could hardly wait to get home and describe the place for the new hogan to his parents.

That night Slim Runner told Mother and Father about the beautiful place he had found. They promised him that they would ride over and look at it the very next day. Then Slim Runner began to tell them about his ideas for the new hogan. Mother smiled, and said, "Be patient, Son. After we have seen the land, we must talk to Uncle. He will help us decide whether we should build a new hogan now."

The mother's brother is a most important member of a Navajo family. A Navajo regards only the people on his mother's side of the family as close relatives.

When Slim Runner's parents saw the land, they decided that this would be the perfect place for a new hogan. That evening they went to visit Uncle. Uncle agreed that it was about time they built a new home. He, too, was sure the old one would not last through the winter. Father said, "It is too bad that we are getting away from the ancient ways of building hogans. The homes we build today are not half as warm in winter. It was easier to keep warm in the old, earth-covered hogans."

"But they were never clean," Mother said. "Sand and dirt were always falling down into our hair and food. A modern hogan is easy to keep clean. We will have a window to let the light in, and a door to keep out the cold."

Uncle said that he would help them build

the hogan. Since he had recently built one for himself, he could show them how to put in the window and the door.

Uncle came the following day. In his pickup truck he brought a load of new logs, a window frame with four panes, and a door. Two neighbors came along to help. Uncle's wife and baby remained behind. "Wife was afraid it would be too cold for the baby. Maybe she will come for the housewarming," Uncle explained. The two neighbors, however, brought their wives. Their children were away at school, and the families looked upon this opportunity to get away from home as a holiday.

The men began to dismantle the old hogan at once. Uncle drove over to the new site and deposited his load of logs. Slim Runner was already there with his herd, and he helped Uncle unload. Soon Uncle was back with another load of logs and some of the family's possessions. By nightfall the pigs, the family household goods, and the lumber from the old hogan and corral had been moved to the new site.

Mother and Sister killed a sheep. The women helped cook some of the meat for the evening meal. It was cold in the open. The women fixed up a place to sleep in the shelter of the logs, and they retired early. The men, wrapped in their blankets, drank hot coffee and sat long by the fire, talking. Slim Runner listened eagerly. Uranium had been found to the east on tribal lands. Gas and oil had been found too. "These will bring great wealth to us," Uncle said.

"Certainly a better future awaits my sons than the poverty most of us have had since childhood," one of the neighbors said. "That is why I sent both of them off to school. Children who do not know the white man's paper talk and the white man's ways will find it hard to get along when they grow up."

"Maybe Slim Runner should also have gone to school," Father said. "But his sister is fifteen, and she will marry soon. We need him here to help us."

"That was my wife's talk, too," the neighbor told Father. But he said no more. A Navajo does not interfere with the decision of another, unless he is related to him. It would have been proper for Uncle, but not for a stranger, to have spoken up with words of advice.

The next morning Slim Runner, as usual, raced with Sister toward the rising sun. He looked at their fresh footprints in the red sand, and thought happily, We are really making all this land ours. We could plant some peach trees near the mesa, to protect them from the wind. And, of course, a patch of corn. Then Mother would not have to buy corn at the trading post.

Meanwhile Mother, with the help of the two women, ground corn for the morning meal, and had hot corncakes ready for Slim Runner and Sister when they returned from the race. The sheep had already spread out to graze.

The sheep dog dozed contentedly in the sun,
and Slim Runner went over to see what he
could do to help with the housebuilding.

First the women swept the circle that marked
the floor of the hogan. They scooped and
scraped away the extra sand and made the
floor even. Then the men laid the first
six logs. The six-sided shape of the hogan
was set. Next they fitted in log after log, making sure that the structure was as tight as they
could make it. Mother, Sister, and the two
women were busy all morning, filling the chinks
between the logs with clay. Slim Runner was
kept busy running back and forth, bringing clay
in a tin pail for them, fetching water to mix
with the clay, and watching the sheep in the
pasture below. By noontime, the men had used
up all the old timbers and were starting to clean
and saw the fresh ones.

At noon everyone rested for a while in the
shade and drank hot coffee. Then Father
clambered up to lay the poles for the roof, and

Uncle handed the men the tar paper to spread over the poles. They left a hole in the center for the chimney. After they had finished laying several layers of tar paper, the men built a chimney of stones, and cemented it with clay. "The higher the chimney, the better the draft," Uncle advised them.

One of the neighbors planed the door. Then they fixed the frame for it, put on the hinges, and hung it. Next they fitted and hammered in the small, four-paned window. By nightfall the hogan was almost ready.

After the men had stopped working, Mother took a large mixing bowl full of corn meal and gave it to Uncle for the housewarming ceremony. Uncle entered the new hogan, holding the bowl in one hand. Everyone watched the ceremony from outside. Slim Runner and Sister, elbowing each other for more room, peered in through the window. Taking a handful of corn meal, Uncle rubbed it against the doorpost.

Corn has sacred properties. Legends tell that out of ears of corn the gods created the ancestors of the Navajo. Corn has good and everlasting qualities. When planted, it increases and spreads. It brings food and growth to the people. The Navajo call this sprinkling of corn meal "gift-giving to the spirits," who may already have entered the hogan or who may enter it later.

Uncle turned to the left and scooped up another handful of corn meal, which he rubbed against the center of the south wall. As he did this he began to chant:

> *"Oojónli cógan*
> May it be delightful in my hogan,
> From my head may it be delightful,
> To my feet may it be delightful,
> Where I lie may it be delightful,
> All about me may it be delightful."

He rubbed corn meal on the west and north

walls. Then he threw some corn meal into the
fire, saying, "May it be delightful and well,
my fire." Standing by the firepit, Uncle tossed
a handful of corn meal upward as a gift to the
sun. Then he said, "May it be delightful, O
Sun, my mother's ancestor." Uncle then
sprinkled corn meal all around the walls,
chanting, "May it be delightful as I walk
around my hogan." Then he sprinkled a handful through the doorway, saying, "May it be
delightful—this road of light to my hogan."

Uncle stepped out of the doorway, and
handed the bowl to Mother. Mother entered
the hogan and began to chant as she sprinkled
corn meal around the hogan:

> "*Oojónli eikóy*
> May it be delightful, my fire.
> May it be delightful for my children.
> May all be well.
> May it be delightful with my food and
>   theirs.

May all be well,
May all of mine be well,
All my flocks, may they be well."

Sister and Slim Runner began to carry in
the household goods. They stacked the old
clothes trunks and the bags, baskets, and bundles
in exactly the same places as before, so that
Mother would be able to find them easily.

Everyone now entered the blessed hogan. The
men sat down in a circle about the fire. The
women carried in a large wooden tray filled
with freshly roasted mutton. The men reached
for the chunks of meat with their fingers, and
began to eat hungrily. Mother poured cups of
hot coffee. Because this was a ceremonial meal,
the other women and Sister did not join the
men. They would eat later.

After the men had finished the meal, Father
passed a package of dried cornhusks, which the
men used instead of paper to roll cigarettes.
Slim Runner, of course, did not smoke; nor was

it the custom for a boy his age to take part in the men's talk. But he, like all Indian boys, was a good listener. He looked up at the dark, arched ceiling, then at the window and the snug wooden door. He smiled at Uncle, and Uncle smiled back at him. "Is it like the picture you made?" he asked.

"Yes, yes," Slim Runner answered. "Now we will all be warm this winter."

"I never saw a boy who so wanted a window in his hogan," Father said, laughing.

A few days later a more formal housewarming ceremony took place. By that time the corrals were finished, and Uncle and his neighbors had returned home. Because so much of the future health and happiness of the people depended on a proper housewarming ceremony, Uncle had asked a shaman (shah'-man)—a Navajo medicine man—to take charge of the ceremony. Uncle brought the shaman to the new hogan. Uncle's wife and baby came too, as well as the neighbors who had helped build the hogan. These guests came not only to honor Slim Runner's family at their housewarming, but also to hear the chants. To attend ceremonies insured a person's good health and happiness.

The shaman and his helpers entered the new hogan and sat down, facing the door and the east. Actually, at a Navajo housewarming, the shaman does not do any of the chanting. It is done by singers. But it is the shaman's responsibility to make sure that the chants are recited letter-perfect, because any omission or error may bring evil upon the household.

The shaman had rehearsed the proper chants with the singers before arrival. He now recited the first line of a chant, and the singers chanted the rest of it. He called in turn upon the spirits: the God of Dawn, White Corn, the God of Twilight, Lightning, the Sun, the Goddess of the East, the God of Pollen, the Gods of Rain. The men paused after each chant. The shaman then recited another line, and the men echoed it with another simple chant.

All through the night the chanting continued. Slim Runner kept adding wood to the fire. The only one in the hogan who slept was Uncle's baby. At the first break of dawn, the chants were finished. All the guests piled into the pickup truck and left.

Slim Runner opened the new door, and darted out after Sister for the morning race toward the rising sun. He caught his breath, on the way back, when he beheld the fresh-looking, handsome hogan, with its smooth roof and its wooden door and window. "How beautiful it is!" he said to himself.

Father had harnessed the horses and was sitting in the wagon waiting for Slim Runner. "Come with me and help with the corn harvest. Sister and Mother will take care of the sheep. They can watch the flock right from the window," Father joked.

Slim Runner jumped up on the wagon, and Father gave him the reins.

2

IN THE HOSPITAL

Within a few days Father and Slim Runner
finished harvesting the corn. Father loaded his
wagon with some of the corn and pumpkins
and left for Chinle, where his mother lived.
He always took part of his harvest to his
mother's hogan. Meanwhile, Mother, Sister,
and Slim Runner hurried to husk their share
of the corn and spread it out to dry on mats,
while the sun was still warm. Mother shelled
some of the ears and put the corn into sacks.
The rest Sister and Slim Runner stacked inside
the hogan and covered with a rug.

Mother cut the squash into strips and hung
them up to dry. By the time Father returned,
the hogan looked like a storage bin: strings of
squash hung from the rafters; corn sacks,

bundles of herbs, and bunches of plants Mother used in dyeing wool were piled in the corners.

"There will be ample food for all this winter," Mother said to Father, trying to cheer herself and the family.

For all was not well, and she was worried. Slim Runner was ill. His body ached and his chest burned. "All has gone well with Slim Runner from the time he was a baby," Mother said. "We had a fine naming ceremony for him. More people attended it than any of the others. What is it that has caused evil to enter his body? Who has bewitched him?"

Illness, in Navajo beliefs, is caused either by witchcraft or by the entrance of some foreign substance into the body; it is cured by a proper ceremony, conducted by a shaman, who removes this evil.

Slim Runner's parents had heard that a curing ceremony, called a Blessingway Ceremony, was being held near Kayenta for a woman who had also been ailing. Like most Navajo ceremonies, or Sings, it would last for nine days. Father and Mother decided that this Blessing-way Ceremony might cure Slim Runner of his illness if he attended it.

Mother arranged for Grandmother to come to stay in the hogan with Sister. They started off with Slim Runner in the wagon, and reached the Sing the following morning. The ceremonial hogan was surrounded by watching people, because they, too, felt confident that their own ailments would leave them if they witnessed the sacred ceremony.

The floor of the large ceremonial hogan was covered with a fresh layer of sand. Several men were already at work on sand paintings. Slim Runner sat down at one end of the hogan, to be out of the way of the sand painters, and watched them paint. He had seen sand paint-ings made before, but now he watched the men with renewed concentration.

Sand painting is an ancient art among In-dians. The Navajo have the reputation for

making the finest sand paintings. Theirs are
the largest and most varied. The paintings illustrate scenes from the Navajo legends—gods,
lightning, sunbeams, rainbows, mountains, and
plants. The colors used in these sand paintings
are the five sacred colors of the Navajo legends:
white, yellow, red, black, and blue. White,
yellow, and red are made of crushed fine sandstone. Black is made of powdered charcoal
mixed with sand. The blue is really a gray
color made of charcoal mixed with white sand.

Slim Runner watched one of the sand painters
as the man crouched on the floor, holding some
black sand between his thumb and first two
fingers. He moved his hand over the ground
and let the sand trickle slowly through his
finger tips in a long, straight line. Toward the
end, the man's hand shook a little, and the line
wavered. He carefully covered the mistake
with a pinch of plain sand, and continued. At
first, the painters were all bunched in the
center of the hogan, where a sand painting is

usually started. But as they progressed, the men separated and spread to different ends of the hogan. The painting took all morning to make.

As soon as it was finished, the ailing woman was brought in and placed in the center of the sand painting. The shaman began chanting as he circled about the woman, who sat with her eyes closed, listening. Slim Runner shut his eyes and listened carefully too, hoping that the ceremony would also cure him. The afternoon passed quickly, and the short winter day was over.

The sand painters gathered up the sand from the paintings in blankets and dumped it outside in a safe place, where it would not be trampled upon. The Navajo destroy their ceremonial sand paintings at the end of each day.

Since this was the last day of the Sing, the ceremony was to end with fire swallowing. Two young fire swallowers arrived late in the afternoon, and Slim Runner looked them over carefully. Outwardly, they looked like two ordinary

Navajo men: they were both tall and thin, with long faces and long hair. Slim Runner stared at them, trying to see if they bore some sign of the sacred power they possessed—the power to hold fire and yet not burn.

When it grew dark, the woman's relatives built a fire outside. Everyone piled out of the ceremonial hogan and sat down facing the fire. The two fire swallowers appeared. They were naked, except for breechcloths. Both had painted their bodies, and they looked black against the blaze. They turned halfway toward the fire, and each plunged a stick into the flames. Then each of the men plunged the end of the burning stick into his open mouth.

The people watched in wonder. Slim Runner remembered the many times during his childhood he had burned himself around the fire in the hogan, despite his mother's warnings. He recalled the pain of burnt finger tips, knees, and toes. The spirits can see how brave they are, the boy thought. Surely no evil spirits dare touch such brave men. Their courage alone is enough to drive off any evil that may have come to the people around them. Their courage is enough to drive out the evil that has entered my body and is giving me such pain. After the ceremony, Slim Runner was so convinced that all his pain had been driven off, that he ate a hearty meal of fresh broiled mutton.

On the way home the next day, Mother said hopefully, "Son is already feeling better." But a few days later, her worries returned. The Blessingway Ceremony had not helped. Slim Runner still looked tired and thin. Mother and Father wondered what they should do. Should they send the boy to a white man's hospital to try the white man's medicine? They were reluctant to put their son, their youngest child, into the hands of strangers whose powers came from strange spirits. Worse evil might befall the boy.

But soon winter was upon them with its cold winds. Slim Runner felt tired all the time.

Father harnessed the wagon, and he and Mother took the boy to the hospital at Kayenta.

At the hospital Slim Runner was X-rayed and given tuberculin tests. The doctor told the parents that he had tuberculosis; but because the disease had not yet seriously injured his lungs, there was a very good chance for complete recovery. He told them that it was well they had brought Slim Runner to the hospital at once, instead of waiting till spring.

As the parents were preparing to leave, the nurse whispered something to them. Both parents quickly turned back for a last look at their son and a last embrace. "They will cut your hair, Son," Mother said.

The Navajo believe that hair has rain power and that to cut a person's hair is to take away his power to help make rain. But the nurse had told Mother the white doctor always insisted that boys' and girls' hair be cut to help them keep clean and get well. Everyone had to obey the orders of the white doctors.

Two months went by. The memory of those first two months in the hospital was hazy and vague to Slim Runner. Then one morning he awoke feeling as tired as though he had been herding sheep all night. Yet he had slept pretty well, better than he had been sleeping for a long time. His chest did not ache any more. He could breathe easily; he felt as though a weight had been lifted from him. And he felt cool.

In his fever during the preceding nights, Slim Runner had often thought that the nurse was his mother. When she said again and again, "Sleep, Son, sleep," the voice sounded just like Mother's. He would open his eyes, thinking his mother had come. But it was always the nurse's white uniform—not Mother's soft, wide skirt and dark blouse. Mother was not too far away, but they had asked her not to come till he felt better.

Today Slim Runner was feeling better, although he was tired. The shiny, white walls of the narrow hospital room hurt his eyes. He closed them wearily and felt his tears sliding out onto the pillow. It felt so good to breathe without pain. Slim Runner was not ashamed of his tears. A Navajo boy is ashamed to cry when he is in pain. Slim Runner had not cried before, not even when he had said good-by to his parents. He could not have cried then or he would have shamed his father and mother. A white doctor and the nurse had been with them, and no Indian likes to show emotion in front of white people. But no man need be too proud to cry when he is happy. So now the boy let his tears trickle down, not caring if anyone saw him.

"You are much better today," the nurse reassured him. She came over to his cot with a basin of water, and began to sponge his face. Slim Runner felt embarrassed at having the nurse wash him. At home he cleansed himself in the sweat house. The men built small, rounded sweat houses of brush and clay. Only

men and boys went inside, naked, to cleanse
themselves by sitting in the hot steam. Then
they rubbed themselves dry with sand. They
did this far away from hogans where a woman
might see them. And here he was being washed
by a strange woman!

Slim Runner heard children's voices and
sudden bursts of laughter next door, in the
ward. He felt lonely and kept wondering what
the children were laughing about. Perhaps tomorrow he would get up enough courage to
ask the nurse when he would be moved there.
Like all Navajo, he disliked being alone. He
had been raised in the midst of many people
and animals and was used to having company
all the time. Even when he was away from the
hogan, herding sheep, he had the companion-
ship of his trusted sheep dog or his horse; and
he came back to his family every evening. Be-
sides, he could never really feel alone outdoors,
where the Cloud Beings were always with him,

changing their shapes all the time as they moved across the sky.

The hospital room was so different from the outdoors, where he could watch the colors of the mesas shift from gold to red, from gray to purple, as the morning passed into noon, and noon into evening. There was so much to see. Each sunrise looked new and different. Each sunset, too, was different from the one before it—not like the sameness of the hospital room.

To be confined to a bed, to rest and stay quiet all day, was most trying to Slim Runner. But that was the only way, the white doctor had said, to fight tuberculosis—the dread disease that had almost cost him his life.

The early sun shining in through the large window already felt hot. The nurse came back with the breakfast tray. She lowered the shade and opened the window halfway. The shade moved slightly in the breeze.

"Eat everything," the nurse said, as she was leaving the room. "When you have finished,

I will bring you a surprise from the doctor."

Slim Runner's eyes opened wide. A surprise? While he ate his breakfast he kept thinking of the nurse's promise. And he finished everything on the tray, even the milk. Slim Runner did not like the taste of cow's milk. At home he drank either goat's milk, whenever it could be spared, or coffee. Here at the hospital the nurse insisted that he drink a glass of milk with every meal. To please her, he gulped the milk down, then bit quickly into a slice of fresh bread to kill the taste. He ate the scrambled egg and saved the thin slice of bacon for last. He liked the smoked, salty bacon, because it reminded him of the smoky smell of Mother's cooking fire.

The food at home, cooked over the open fire, always had a smoky smell to it. It lacked salt as compared to the hospital food. The Navajo dug for salt in the Zuni Salt Lakes, but they used it sparingly.

After breakfast, Slim Runner was supposed

to rest, but he was feeling so much better that he decided not to take a nap. The nurse took away his tray and came back with two packages. She helped Slim Runner open the first one. It was a box of crayons. He counted them eagerly. "Twenty-four!" he cried. Each crayon was a different shade. How beautiful they were! The nurse propped up the box so he could admire them. The second package was heavy, and the nurse opened it for Slim Runner. His thin, long fingers shook with anticipation. He hoped it was paper, and it was. The only paper he had ever had before came from Older Brother's notebook. The nurse tilted one end of the box, and showed Slim Runner how to place a sheet of paper on the cardboard so it would rest firmly.

Slim Runner felt very happy. Now that he had crayons and paper, he would be able to make drawings. He would be kept busy, and then he wouldn't feel so lonely.

He was so excited that he almost forgot to ask the nurse to thank the doctor. After she

had left his room, Slim Runner studied the
crayons carefully. Which color should he use
first? He almost chose the gay turquoise; instead, he turned to the shades of brown, and
finally settled on a terra cotta color. He made
a few lines on the fresh white paper, and then
paused. He wanted to be very sure. Although
he had drawn many pictures before, in sand
and on scraps of paper Older Brother had given
him, this was the first time he had ever used a
sheet of blank new paper. Perhaps he would
draw the mesas first, the flat-topped hills that
he faced each day when he awoke and went
outside. Always from behind the mesas the
sun rose from its daily sleep and lighted them
with a bright orange color.

After he had shaped the mesas, Slim Runner
began to draw the green cottonwood trees that
grew by the river. He first selected a dark
green crayon, but the dark green made too
strong a contrast with the warm, light terra
cotta. He chose a pale green shade instead, and

then used a gray crayon to shape the trunk and branches.

To show the sun shining over the trees, Slim Runner first tried a pale yellow crayon. He drew several circles with it, as he had seen Navajo men do in sand painting. But the yellow circles looked too dull against the green. So Slim Runner erased the yellow lines. He picked up the turquoise pencil and again drew several circles. Now the sun looked exactly as it did in the sand paintings, and Slim Runner was pleased.

He next drew some fanlike bunches of sage with a green crayon. Then he took a brown crayon and began to outline the new six-sided hogan. As always, Mother sat outside the hogan near the piñon tree, weaving. The rug she was making was almost finished. He made the rug very colorful: red, pink, and yellow stripes. He finished it with a white-and-black border.

Sister and Grandmother sat near Mother. Slim Runner did not put Father in the picture, because Father and Grandmother had to avoid each other. According to a Navajo custom, a mother-in-law must never speak to her son-in-law or look at him. Grandmother had moved to Uncle's hogan as soon as Mother had married and brought Father to live with her. She usually came to visit when Father was not at home.

Slim Runner could almost hear his mother starting her day's weaving with a song that was also a prayer to the spirits for inspiration. He began to hum the song she always sang:

> May it be beautiful before me.
> May it be beautiful behind me.
> May it be beautiful below me.
> May it be beautiful above me.
> May it be beautiful all around me.

At first Slim Runner had planned to draw Mother in her everyday, rather worn skirt and blouse. But he soon realized that this wouldn't do. Mother would be displeased. Navajo like to be seen in their best clothes. He quickly pulled out the turquoise crayon. She would wear her turquoise-colored skirt and her best purple velvet blouse. Slim Runner decorated Mother's blouse with rows of silver buttons. He added a generous number of necklaces of silver and turquoise, and then drew a pair of earrings, several bracelets, and a wide silver belt.

Slim Runner was tired now. Happy with his morning's work, he put the box down to make room for the lunch tray. The Navajo cook had slaughtered a sheep and had broiled the mutton in an open fire, just the way it was cooked at home. Slim Runner liked to eat the meat with his fingers. It was hard for him to handle the knife and fork Nurse always put on his tray and said he must learn to use. He used a spoon well, because there were spoons in the hogan. But solid food was always picked up with the finger tips at home. So Slim Runner waited for the nurse to leave before he started eating.

He drank his milk first, then ate the cooked carrots with his fingers. He regarded the meat as dessert and ate it at the end of the meal, together with the canned peaches. As soon as his tray was taken away, Slim Runner drew the bed sheet over his head (just as he always drew the sheepskin over his head at home), and was soon sound asleep.

After his nap, Slim Runner drew horses for the rest of the afternoon. The Navajo's love of horses is well known. In their legends the gods created the horse. The Navajo say:

> The horse was created of the dawn—the white and the black.
> His heart was made of red stone,
> Of lightning his ears,
> Of twinkling stars his eyes,
> Of white shell his teeth,
> Of beads his lips.
> His tail was made of black rain.
> His feet they made of a cloud;

His gait, of a rainbow,
And his bridle, of sun strings.

Only a boy who had observed horses from babyhood and loved them could have drawn all the postures and detailed movements Slim Runner had put into his pictures. His horses had long, flowing manes that reached to the ground. There were horses of many breeds and colors; prancing horses with proud, arched necks; horses leaping through the air; horses with flaring, fiery nostrils and the long, thin legs of racers. And always in the background were Slim Runner's beloved mesas and their wind-twisted trees and shrubs.

The doctor and the nurse came in for their daily round. The doctor spent quite a long time studying the drawings and talking about them to the nurse. He thought they were very good. The nurse translated his remarks to Slim Runner.

Encouraged by the white doctor's praise,

Slim Runner drew a picture of his own horse; but he thinned its legs a little and lengthened its mane and tail. The horse came out a much nobler and younger creature than he actually was. For the first time since he had come to the hospital, Slim Runner's thoughts turned to his horse without a pang. He was no longer lonely.

Several nights later, Slim Runner was sitting up in bed, listening to the winds that howled and whipped about the mesa, piling snowdrifts against the hospital building. Only a corner of his room was lit by a small lamp; the rest was in total darkness. It reminded him of the hogan, where the only circle of light on winter evenings came from the small firepit in the center of the room. He thought of his family, sitting together by the fire, after the evening meal. On nights like this, Father would tell the sacred stories of the Navajo in a low voice, after first glancing about the hogan to make sure that the door was closed.

These sacred stories have to be told indoors. No one knows when a spirit, good or evil, might be listening through an open door. The spirit might be offended with something said by the storyteller, and might bring evil to the people inside. That is why these sacred stories are told in winter, when families gather indoors.

The Navajo, like many other tribes who have no written language, transmit the history of their people through stories, told from generation to generation. We call these stories myths and legends, and when we use those words we mean that not all of the stories are entirely true. But the Navajo believe that everything in their stories is true. To them, these stories out of the far past are sacred. They cover everything that touches the lives and minds of the Navajo: gods and giants; magic and supernatural things; the creation of the sun, moon, earth, and mountains; animals and man; and heroes, both human and animal, who shaped the Navajo past. These stories are the

basis for the Navajo beliefs today—their re-
ligion.

The next morning Slim Runner decided to
draw pictures to illustrate these stories. He
worked all that day on the first two pictures;
they were not finished and put away until just
before the evening meal. Slim Runner began
to live in another world—the world of the
sacred stories.

Now the boy no longer counted the days
since he had left home. He knew that many
days had gone by, because he had almost used
up his package of paper. The long winter was
almost over. Spring was in the air. Father
would soon be working in his cornfield. The
sheep would be sheared, and the women would
be busy carding wool.

Slim Runner was permitted to get up to
wash himself now, and to eat his meals at the
little table.

"You are much better," Nurse told him,
smiling as usual. "You are a good patient. Soon

you will go to the ward with the other children." Then she asked, "By the way, what are
you doing these days? You haven't shown me
your paintings for a long time. I know you
are drawing all the time. Don't you want to
show me your pictures any more?"

Slim Runner did not want Nurse to think
that he was hiding his drawings from her.
These drawings were designs for sand paintings,
and they were sacred. He could not show them
to anyone now. He tried to explain this to the
nurse. "It is not possible for me to tell you
what I am painting. I will show you the paintings when the time is right. The time now is
not right."

Being a Navajo, Nurse understood. The
Navajo respect other people's feelings and
preferences. The next day Nurse brought Slim
Runner a stiff cardboard envelope in which to
keep his finished drawings.

The next time the doctor examined Slim
Runner, he remarked to the nurse how happy

and contented the boy seemed, and how quickly he was recovering.

"He will soon need more paper and more crayons," Nurse said.

"I will buy him some water colors," the doctor promised. When the nurse interpreted this for Slim Runner, he nearly jumped out of bed for joy.

The boy did very little drawing during the next few days. He waited for the water colors. Some years ago, his parents had taken Slim Runner to Gallup, to see the annual Intertribal Ceremonials. At a store in Gallup he had seen water-color paintings for the first time. The storekeeper had told the boy that these were made by Indian artists, and that many of the artists were Navajo.

The box of water colors arrived at last. For a while the work went very slowly. The boy had to learn how to use the brushes. But working with water colors, Slim Runner soon discovered, was much more satisfying than working with crayons. He could now use many more shades, and his drawings became more brilliant and gay. As the days went by, his pile of paintings grew. At last he had made pictures for as many sacred stories as he could remember. Each time he finished a painting, he carefully tucked it into the envelope Nurse had given him. When he completed the last painting, he sealed the envelope—to be opened when the time was right.

3

AT THE TRADING POST

For the first time since he had come to the hospital, Slim Runner was allowed outside with his lunch tray. He sat on a bench with the other children, his back against the warm, adobe wall of the hospital, enjoying the spring sunshine and the food. When the pitcherful of milk was passed around, Slim Runner filled his glass for the second time. The cool milk had a sweet, refreshing taste, and he wondered how he could have disliked it so at first. But all food tasted so much better outdoors, in the warm sun and cool breeze. He smelled the junipers and the sage, and thought, I can put all this beauty into my pictures, but I cannot paint the smells!

For the first time, too, the nurse took him

to the doctor's office for his daily check up.
Slim Runner's eyes almost popped out of his
head when he entered the office. Two of his
drawings, one of horses and the other a land-
scape, were framed on the wall behind the
doctor's desk. During the winter Slim Runner
had asked the nurse to choose a few of his
paintings to give to the doctor. It was his way
of thanking the white man for the water colors.
The boy had had no idea that the doctor would
like them so much.

After the examination, the doctor said to
Slim Runner, "You are well now and can go
home any time." Then he talked to him about
the paintings. "They are excellent, Son. Nurse
and I will speak to your parents when they
come to take you home. You should go to art
school. Someday you will be a great artist, and
your people will be proud of you."

The doctor's words made Slim Runner very
happy. It would be wonderful to be back with
his family again, and he was pleased that the

doctor had admired his paintings. But he realized that it probably would not be possible for him to go to art school. He was needed at home. Older Brother had given up school to take care of the sheep while Slim Runner was in the hospital, but he would go back to school when Slim Runner came home. Sister would probably marry soon, and then she would have to attend to her own household. Mother had to work steadily at the weaving, or they would have no money for groceries. When Father had any time to spare from his work in the cornfield, he went to his own mother's hogan, because a Navajo is brought up to help his mother's people. Slim Runner would be the only one in the family who could take care of the flock. It is more important to help Mother than to draw pictures, he decided.

The nurse broke in on his thoughts, and suggested that he go outdoors again and sit in the sun. "You're so pale that you look like a white boy," she teased him, knowing that a

Navajo wants to look like a Navajo, not like a white man.

Outside, the children were running and laughing. A group of boys and girls were playing ball. Another group were playing an old game called hoop and pole. The boys had sticks which they threw at a rolling hoop. When a player succeeded in sending his stick through the hoop without disturbing the hoop's motion, he won a point for his team. In a few days Slim Runner hoped to be able to join the game. For the present he had to remain an onlooker who shouted encouragement to the players. It felt good to laugh and shout again.

A small boy sitting next to Slim Runner took a string out of his pocket and offered to play cat's cradle with him. The two soon became absorbed in this ancient Indian game. The little boy knew some figures, but not as many as Slim Runner knew. He was delighted to learn how to make a few more patterns and how to take them off Slim Runner's fingers.

They played for a long time, executing figure after figure, till the small boy was called in for his rest.

"Thank you, Older Brother," he said, as a nurse took his hand and led him inside. "I will be here tomorrow, too, if you want to play this with me."

"I will be here too, Younger Brother." Slim Runner patted him on the back. He was glad he could help the boy feel less lonely.

For a while Slim Runner watched the ball game. Two boys got into an argument over the ball, and started wrestling on the grass. The girls picked up the ball and began to play catch. Slim Runner watched them for a while. They were so pretty in their long, wide skirts and velveteen blouses trimmed with silver buttons.

Slim Runner watched them, because of the colorful picture they presented. I'll try to put it down on paper, he thought. He rushed inside, took out his box of papers and crayons, and was back in a jiffy, sketching the players. Soon several boys were bending over his pad of paper, admiring the drawing. "You do it very well," they praised him. The wrestlers, seeing the crowd about Slim Runner, stopped their fighting and came over too. "It is beautiful," they agreed.

After the evening meal, when the nurse had come to prepare the children for bed, Slim Runner gave her the picture he had drawn that afternoon. The nurse held it up admiringly. "It is a thing of beauty," she said quietly. "I am most happy to have it. Tomorrow I will show you how to write your name. You must sign your pictures, the way all artists do."

In the days that followed, Slim Runner sat in the sunshine, drawing pictures of the children at play. They always invited him to join their games, and he sometimes played ball with the boys. But he still tired quickly and returned to his drawings.

Slim Runner's parents arrived in the middle

of the summer to take him home. Father had left Older Brother to tend the cornfield, and Mother had left Sister and Grandmother to tend the sheep and care for the household. While the nurse and doctor talked to his parents, Slim Runner rolled up his few belongings in a blanket. He packed his paintings, the box of water colors, and the crayons in newspaper, and placed the bundles in the wagon. He stood patting the familiar horses as, one after another, the children came over to say good-by and wish him well.

Slim Runner and his parents climbed into the comfortable wagon, which looked like a prairie schooner with its stained white canvas top; and the team of horses started briskly along the dusty trail.

"We are going to the trading post before we go home," Mother told Slim Runner. "I have three rugs to trade, and I want to buy groceries. You will need good food to keep you well."

Slim Runner was happy to be leaving the hospital. He had been away from home for many months. Mother and Father kept patting him affectionately. They were pleased that he had grown so tall and had put on weight. The doctor had told them that the evil sickness that had entered his lungs and made him cough had now left him completely. With good care, good food, and good rest, Slim Runner would remain well.

Mother made Slim Runner tie a kerchief over his nose and mouth, so he would not inhale the dust and start coughing again. "This land was grassy once," she said. "There was no dust then."

"Now it is always like this in dry summer," Father said. "And we can't go on the paved road, because these horses will shy at the cars and run away. Crawl inside, Son, and get some sleep."

It was cool inside the wagon and filled with familiar smells: the family's bedrolls, Father's saddle, a small sack of dried meat and corn bread. Slim Runner stretched out for a quick nap; but he soon peered out again, anxious not to miss too much of the journey.

The sun was setting as they reached the familiar trading post. Men, women, and children in pickup trucks, on horseback, and in wagons were coming and going. Many people knew Slim Runner and his parents, and greeted them. Mother shook the dust off her skirt and blouse and tightened her shawl about her, before entering the trading post.

To the Navajo, the low wooden buildings housed all the treasures of the white man's world. The crowded shelves held all kinds of canned fruits and vegetables. Near the counter were sacks of beans, peas, corn, wheat, flour, and sugar. In one section were kerosene lamps and lanterns. There were plates and cups, pots and pans, and silverware. In another section were shelves filled with bright Pendleton blankets, which every Navajo likes to own. There were also goods by the yard—cottons, woolens, nylons, and velveteens. And finally, there was ready-made clothing—jeans, cotton and rayon shirts, jackets, and cowboy boots and hats.

Mother waited her turn at the counter. She listened carefully to the trader, to see how much he would pay the weaver ahead of her for a rug. Father did not come in with her. It was not customary for a man to help his wife trade her rugs. The rugs she made belonged to her, and she traded them.

Mother placed the folded rug on the counter. She left it to the trader to unfold it. He did this with anticipation and care. At the first touch he could always tell whether a rug would be exceptional, or just another Navajo rug; and he knew immediately by the fine, tight weave that Mother's rug was superior. It had pale yellow, pink, and blue stripes, without any border. The stripes were as even as if they had been measured with a ruler instead of with Mother's experienced eye and old batten sticks.

"You have a fine rug," the trader said in Navajo.

"I have tried to make it beautiful," Mother answered modestly.

The trader went over to the cash register, took out seven silver dollars, and placed them on the counter next to the rug.

Mother did not even bother to count the silver. She knew by the size of the pile that it was not the ten dollars she had expected. With the carding, spinning, and dyeing, it had taken her many, many days to make the rug. But Mother did not bargain with the trader. She picked up the rug and started to fold it.

"Do you have another rug?" the trader asked.

Mother motioned to Slim Runner to bring in the second rug. This one was black and white, with a strip of red inside the black border, and much larger than the first rug.

The trader smiled with pleasure. He called over to the old Navajo clerk, "Come and see a fine rug." The two men admired the rug. The trader went to the cash register and took out another handful of silver dollars. He added three dollars to the first pile of silver, and put fifteen silver dollars near the large rug.

The trading had taken a more favorable turn. Mother motioned to Slim Runner to bring in the last rug. It was brown, gray, and white, very much like the famous Navajo Two Gray Hills rugs, which fetch top prices wherever rugs are sold. The trader put a pile of fifteen silver dollars next to the last rug, too, after the Navajo clerk had admired it.

Mother felt that the large rug should have brought her twenty dollars. But since the trader had raised the price on the first one to ten, and had given her fifteen for the second, she did not feel she should bargain about the third. The trader would think her greedy. She tied the silver coins into a corner of her kerchief, moved to the grocery shelves, and began to point out to the clerk what she wanted.

Next Mother went to the goods-by-the-yard section, where she selected a bright nylon for a skirt for Sister. She wanted enough velveteen to make two blouses, one for herself and one for Sister; but the velveteen cost over three dollars a yard. So she bought only enough material for Sister.

Mother saw Slim Runner admiring the cowboy boots, but they were too expensive. "I would rather have a pair of work shoes," Slim Runner lied bravely. Mother chose a pair of heavy shoes for him. She regretted that she had no money left to buy bright kerchiefs for Older Brother and for Father. Instead, she bought fifty cents' worth of hard candy, and told Slim Runner that she was ready to go home.

It was already dark. While waiting for Mother, Father had watered the horses. He helped Mother and Slim Runner pack their bundles into the wagon, and the family started for home. The horses were now on familiar ground and required little guidance from the driver.

Here and there by the roadside, families were camping for the night. The women had small cooking fires going and were bending over them, preparing the evening meal. Men sat nearby, smoking and talking. Hobbled horses grazed in the dark. Pickup trucks were parked near some of the groups. The people who owned the pickup trucks could have driven home easily; but they preferred to spend the night outdoors, in the clear summer air.

Mother and Father were already dozing. Slim Runner was getting sleepy too. He looked up at the sky, at the scattered stars, and thought of how First Woman had mixed them up. Father had told him the story one winter night.

First Man and First Woman created the sun out of clear stone. They set around it precious turquoise, rays of red rain, lightning, and snakes of many kinds to bring the rain. They carved the moon out of a piece of crystal and

bordered it with white shells. Over its face
they put sheets of lightning and water of all
kinds and colors. But after the sun had set and
the moon had not yet come up, it was dark
again. To make some light, First Man and
First Woman gathered pieces of sparkling mica.
First Man laid these out in a pleasing design.
A special piece of mica represented the North
Star. Next he made a pattern of seven more
pieces of mica for the Big Dipper. He selected
a large piece to represent the planet Mars; some
distance from it he placed the planet Jupiter.
First Man was getting tired from all this work,
and so he lay down for a nap.

First Woman, impatient with all the clutter
in their hogan, gathered together the remaining
pieces of mica and threw them upward. They
scattered all over the sky, every which way,
forming twinkling stars. First Man was quite
angry when he awoke and saw what First
Woman had done. "Someday," he said, "I must
pull these pieces down and rearrange them into

a more pleasing pattern." But somehow he never had the time to do this. So the stars have remained scattered in the sky to this day, waiting to be properly placed.

It would certainly be a lot of work to arrange all these, Slim Runner thought, looking up at the sky. His eyelids felt heavy, and he, too, dozed off.

4

HOME AGAIN

Later that evening, the travelers arrived at home. Older Brother rushed out of the hogan, and Sister and Grandmother followed him. Grandmother stood with her back to the wagon, to avoid looking at Father. Slim Runner, still sleepy, clambered from the wagon, and in a moment was in Grandmother's arms. Older Brother joyfully slapped him on the back in greeting. Sister hugged the bundle of dress goods Mother had given her. She greeted Slim Runner more formally. "Welcome back to our hogan," she said. Sister looked so grown-up that Slim Runner felt shy with her, and said quietly, "I am happy to be home."

There was a homey smell of mutton, leather, and fresh corn bread in the hogan. Slim Runner inhaled the smells, and was glad to be back among the familiar things. Sister and Older Brother popped pieces of candy into their mouths, and then proceeded to put away the bundles Mother had brought from the trading post. It was too dark to go out to look at the sheep, so Slim Runner sat down by the fire on his old sheepskin.

Sister spread a grass mat on the floor by the firepit. While Father and Brother were un-hitching the wagon, Mother and Grandmother put on the mat slices of fresh store bread, some corn bread, a can of tomatoes, a can of con-densed milk for the coffee, some slices of cold mutton and cheese, and cups and spoons. As soon as Father came inside and sat down, Grandmother turned away from the fire and ate the meal with her back to the family.

Navajo families do not usually linger over their meals, but this evening the meal lasted a long time. One by one, the family asked Slim Runner about his stay in the hospital. Slim

Runner described in detail his daily life there: the food he had eaten, the children he had met, the white doctor and the kind Navajo nurse, and how he had spent the time painting pictures.

After the dishes had been cleared and wiped clean, Older Brother lit the kerosene lamp and brought over Slim Runner's package of pictures. The family crowded around him to look at them. Slim Runner showed the family his first picture—the hogan. All three women exclaimed, "It is a thing of beauty!" Then each, in turn, closely examined herself in the picture, admiring the colors, the clothes, and the jewelry. "This is as we like to look," Mother said.

Older Brother was most enthusiastic about the drawings of horses, which Slim Runner showed them next. "How alive they look!" he said over and over. "Many boys in my school draw well too. The teacher says that we, the Dineh, are born artists. But none of the boys draw as well as you do, Younger Brother."

The drawings were passed from hand to hand. Everyone admired the landscapes. "Here is where we camped," Sister said, examining the picture of Monument Valley. "Here is where we attended that Sing, when you were. . . ." Mother quickly caught herself and left the sentence unfinished. One must not speak of illness. Now that it was over, it should be forgotten, so that it wouldn't recur. "Here is where we were sheepherding last spring," Sister pointed out, as she looked at the next drawing.

Slim Runner got up and shut the door of the hogan before he opened the brown envelope that held the sacred paintings. The family knew at once that here was something special, and everyone edged closer to the kerosene lamp. Slim Runner explained how he had come to paint these sacred paintings last winter. Father and Mother were convinced, even before he had finished talking, that it was his painting of sacred subjects that had helped Slim Runner

get well. Thinking of sacred things is like pray-
ing, and it brings health and happiness.

In silence, almost as though they were wit-
nessing a sacred ceremony, the family passed
the pictures from hand to hand and examined
them. "These are all true, just like the sand
paintings," Father commented, studying the de-
tails of the pictures.

The lamp began to splutter. It was time for
bed. Grandmother took her bedroll and went
outside to sleep in the wagon. Sister picked up
her bedroll and went out to keep Grandmother
company. Slim Runner, too, wanted to sleep
outdoors, but Mother said it might get cold or
damp during the night. Unaccustomed to the
hard floor and too excited by all the praise he
had received from his family, the boy lay awake
for a while. But he slept very well when he
finally did fall asleep.

The day in the hogan began, as always, just
before the sun rose. When Slim Runner threw
off his cover, Older Brother put a restraining

hand on him. "Mother would like you to rest today. I'll run with Sister." He dressed and left. Mother came in from the corral with a pail of goat's milk. She left the door of the hogan open. The sun streamed in, warming the room. Slim Runner rolled up his bed and sat against the wall, drinking the warm goat's milk and enjoying the sunshine. A little later Older Brother came back to get the herd and take them out to graze. Slim Runner noted that there were many sheep and goats in the herd that were new to him. We will have to get acquainted all over again, Slim Runner thought.

Uncle came at noon to take Grandmother home, but Mother asked her to stay a while longer. "It is time we held a ceremony for Sister. She has come of age. She will want her grandmother to help with the ceremony."

The ceremony of Sister's coming into womanhood took four days. She still raced each morning toward the rising sun. Each day, after the race, Grandmother massaged Sister all over in a molding ceremony. This was done so that Sister would grow up into a beautiful woman. While the ceremony was taking place, the men of the family had to stay away from the shelter they had built for Sister. She was not permitted to see anyone except Grandmother and Mother. During the day she kept busy carding wool, spinning, sewing, and mending. This was to show the spirits that she liked work and hoped the spirits would reward her.

On the third day, Sister started grinding the corn for a very large corncake that would be served with the feast at the end of the four-day ceremony. Mother and Grandmother dug a pit, heated it, and lined it with cornhusks. Sister mixed water into the corn meal, and poured the batter into the pit. The pit was then sealed with grass, and the corncake remained in the pit to steam for twenty-four hours. Sister served the cake to her family at the end of the fourth day, together with broiled meat, canned peaches, and hot coffee.

Grandmother left the family a few days later. The children were sorry to see her leave, but they all agreed that Father would feel freer with Grandmother gone. Things get complicated in a one-room house when two people have to keep avoiding each other.

That evening the father and son of a family that used to live to the north of the hogan came to ask for Sister in marriage. They brought gifts with them—wool for Mother and two horses for Father. The young man was called White Horse. He and Sister had often played together when they were little. Slim Runner had forgotten all about White Horse and was surprised to see him grown-up and so handsomely dressed. White Horse had worked for a while with a road gang and had bought himself nice clothes, a few good horses, and a handsome silver-inlaid saddle. The young man wore a pair of heavy Levis, with a wide silver belt, a bright rayon shirt, cowboy boots, and a cowboy's hat. Thus dressed, and with a small bundle of personal belongings and a bedroll tied to his saddle, he was ready to move in with his bride's people—if accepted.

He was accepted, and the simple marriage ceremony took place two weeks later. The groom and a few of his friends, Father, Uncle, and the boys, built a hogan for the newlyweds. The couple's hogan was nearby. Sister insisted on having her hogan close enough so that she could work with Mother on rugs. To Slim Runner's delight, Sister's hogan had two windows in it, as well as a door.

The marriage celebration took place on the evening when the new hogan was finished. At sunset many people began arriving for the dance. They came in wagons and pickup trucks and on horseback. Families with small children spread blankets and built tiny cooking fires for their evening meal. An enterprising Navajo erected a brush shelter with a firepit in it for roasting a sheep. Slim Runner and Older Brother gathered a pile of brush and dry wood and built a fire in the center of a circle. Young girls, dressed in their finest and chaperoned by their mothers, sat near the fire, waiting for the men to appear.

Girls customarily start the dance by inviting the men to dance with them. If a man does not wish to accept an invitation, he gives the girl a coin. If he accepts, the two circle together a few times—heel and toe—around the fire. When a man wants to stop dancing, he has to pay his partner. If he continues dancing with her, it means that he likes her. And then and there the older women, sitting around the fire watching their daughters, begin making plans for the couple's future.

The music for the dance was provided by a drummer and a chorus of male voices. The drummer sat on a blanket within the circle of dancers. The chorus, a group of men and boys, stood shoulder to shoulder, away from the fire and the spectators. They pulled their broad-brimmed hats over their foreheads and swayed

in rhythm to the drumbeat. The singing—a melody without words—was broken at regular intervals by a falsetto note, with a strange, haunting quality.

Beyond the circle, all was now in darkness. A crowd of people wrapped in blankets sat quietly on the sidelines. Some were watching the dancers; others were dozing. The young couples, now lit up by the fire, now shadowed in darkness, kept moving around and around inside the circle, their arms about each other's waists as they danced—heel and toe—to the drumbeat.

The dance lasted till dawn. But long before that, Sister and her husband had slipped quietly away to their new hogan. Slim Runner and Older Brother, however, got no sleep at all that night. Both were busy keeping the fire going. Early in the morning, they fetched water and a load of hay for the sheep in the corral. With the sheep taken care of, the family retired to their own hogan, to sleep.

5

WORKING WITH SILVER

The next winter was a most eventful one for Slim Runner. He attended several Sings with his mother and father. His parents were still anxious to have Slim Runner with them during these Sings, to make sure that he would stay well and happy. He always carried his drawing pad with him. People made room for the boy at these ceremonies, so that he could watch the proceedings at close range. Everyone knew that he was good at painting, better than most Navajo were. Almost every Navajo child could draw, and had a good sense of design; but Slim Runner was really gifted, they said. They compared his paintings to those of well-known Navajo artists and predicted that someday he would be a great artist too. At these ceremonies Slim Runner sold several of his designs to the singers and to the men who did sand paintings.

In the evenings Father and Mother would often invite a few men and their wives to the warm hogan to talk, tell stories, and play games. Their favorite was a guessing game, called the moccasin game. Four moccasins were placed before a player, and he had to guess which moccasin a bone was hidden in. The players and onlookers made small bets. Slim Runner liked to watch the game, and he often sketched the players by the light of the kerosene lantern. Once Father bet two of these drawings on a game. The winners were quite pleased to receive the drawings; and this, in turn, pleased Father.

When the people gathered again for a game, Father asked Slim Runner to show them some of the designs for sand paintings he had made at the hospital. One of the neighbors, a shaman, asked Slim Runner to let him show the paintings to three young men he was coaching for a Sing. In exchange, the shaman took off his heavy silver bracelet and gave it to the boy. "When you are older, Son," he said gratefully, "I will show you how to make sand paintings at ceremonies. With your talent and sure hand, you will make a fine craftsman."

Uncle was at the hogan that evening. When he heard the shaman's words, he turned to Slim Runner, and said, "Yes, it is good for you to learn to make sand paintings for ceremonies. But you also want to help your parents. A man nowadays cannot make a living by being an artist or a sand painter. Your mother and father do not have enough land to farm, and they need money with which to buy more sheep. Your mother has talked to me about this. I think you would make a good silversmith, and I am willing to teach you. There is always a great demand for jewelry. You can work with me during the summer and earn some money."

During the next few months Slim Runner

thought over his uncle's words. He had known that it would be almost impossible for him to go to art school, but he had still hoped that some way might be found. He loved to paint, and he was heavyhearted at the thought of working as a silversmith. But he was fourteen now, and knew he must help the family by earning money.

Early in the summer Uncle came to get Slim Runner. The boy packed his bedroll in the pickup truck. Uncle drove on ahead, and Slim Runner followed on horseback. He was greeted at the hogan by Grandmother and Uncle's wife, who was glad to have a boy about the house to help her with small chores.

The first day or two Slim Runner just watched quietly as Uncle went about his day's work. Each night the anvil, the tools, and the box of silver bars and chips had to be put away to make room for eating the evening meal, for visitors, and for the bedrolls. Each morning the tools were unpacked. Uncle always sat on the floor on a saddle blanket, with his anvil in front of him and his tools arranged beside him on the floor. Uncle had many tools for silversmithing. He had bought some of them at the trader's; others he had made himself. There were several kinds of pliers, saws, tweezers, wrenches, tin snips, many other tools and materials, and a bundle of various dies. Uncle liked to arrange his tools in order, so he would not have to search for one when he needed it.

Within a few days Slim Runner knew how to prepare Uncle's work corner for him. He began by pushing the heavy, low anvil nearer to the opened door, so that Uncle could work in a good light. Light was important for his work. Uncle had put two windows in his hogan so he could work by natural light even in the winter, when the family had to shut the door to keep warm. Slim Runner arranged the tools, and then brought out the special box containing the silver for the jewelry.

The silver consisted of small bars, weighing

about an ounce each, which Uncle bought at the trading post whenever he went there to turn in the jewelry he had made and to receive new orders for jewelry. Uncle could not keep up with these orders from the trader. He was always behind, and the trader kept urging him to work harder. But Uncle would not work harder. He still liked to attend to his cornfield and to bring home the fresh corn, the squashes, and the peppers, which added variety to the meals in the hogan. He liked to spend some time with friends and relatives, and to listen to their criticisms of his work and their suggestions for improvement. And he also liked to go to dances and to Sings. He was sure that the reason he was well and able to do such good work was because he attended these ceremonies. Uncle knew that he could turn out more work if he cared less about workmanship and design. But he preferred to do fewer and better pieces, and to vary the design on each bracelet, ring, necklace, and pair of earrings.

After Slim Runner had set up Uncle's work corner, he got the fire ready. He filled a tin bucket with charcoal and added a few coals from the cooking fire. He put a crucible filled with silver into the bucket, and then worked the bellows for a few minutes to fan the flame onto the charcoal. The charcoal heated the silver in the crucible, and it began to melt. Uncle and Slim Runner sat down on the folded saddle blankets and watched the silver melt. It would take about a half hour for silver to melt by this process, and it had to be timed just right.

Uncle was making a bracelet. He had made a mold for it by filing a piece of soft lava and lining it with sheep tallow, so the silver would not stick to the stone. The mold was only about three inches long. Uncle placed the mold on top of the anvil. Then, with a pair of tongs, he lifted the crucible from the hot coals and poured the melted silver into the mold.

When the silver in the mold had cooled

sufficiently, he removed it from the mold and began to hammer it until the metal had spread to an even thickness. "Pounding," he explained to Slim Runner, "hardens the silver. But silver must not be pounded if it is too cold. Then it will harden unevenly and will crack." When Uncle felt that the bracelet had cooled too much, he laid the silver on his asbestos sheet and with his blowtorch heated it again. Then he let it cool for a little while before he continued the pounding. The metal became thinner and wider under the pounding, till it was about eight inches long.

Actually the finished bracelet would be slightly shorter, about seven inches. Since Navajo men wear as much jewelry as the women do, most bracelets are made to fit the wider, masculine wrist.

Uncle now took a ruler and measured a line along the edge of the bracelet. With a cold chisel he made a groove along the line he had marked and cut along the groove with tin

shears. He repeated the same process along all
the edges and filed them till they were per-
fectly smooth and rounded. Slim Runner carefully swept the silver filings into a can. These
would be melted again when Uncle was ready
to start another piece.

With a die Uncle had made out of an old
scrap of iron, he impressed designs on the bracelet. He put the straight piece of silver on a
rounded log and bent it against the wood. Now
the bracelet would fit a wrist, and it was almost
finished. But Uncle was called away to a
neighbor's hogan, so he and Slim Runner didn't
resume work until the next day.

The silver had become coated with a black
film of soot. Uncle heated the bracelet on his
asbestos sheet and dipped it into a bowl of nitric
acid, which turned the silver a dull gray. Next
he rubbed the bracelet slightly on the dirt floor
and buffed it with a piece of buckskin. He
then dipped it into water, rubbed it with a wire
brush, and finished the polishing with a sprin-

kling of jeweler's rouge. The bracelet now had a high polish.

A shiny silver bracelet like the one Uncle had made was quite acceptable to the Indians, who like their jewelry bright. But tourists prefer their silver with a duller finish. Since the bracelet was for the trader, who would probably sell it to tourists, Uncle dipped it into a sulphur solution. The bracelet blackened. He again buffed it with a piece of buckskin until it had just the right finish.

Although Slim Runner had not been anxious to learn silversmithing, he had watched Uncle's work with growing interest. Now he examined the finished bracelet thoughtfully, and said, "It is truly beautiful, and made with great care. I, too, would like to make such a beautiful piece."

The next day Uncle let him use a few of the files. The boy quickly learned how to handle them. Three days later Uncle handed Slim Runner a silver pendant which he had been working on and asked him to rub it down.

While Slim Runner rubbed the pendant, Uncle began to scrape a mold for making a ketoh (ke'-taw). A ketoh is a wide bow guard worn today by the Navajo men as an ornament. A Navajo will not hesitate to trade several horses for a desired ketoh.

Uncle wore a ketoh himself. It was an old design. Inside the heavy, square silver rim were two bows, joined back to back. In the center was a large, heavy stone. He valued the ketoh because of its simple design, and because it was one of the first made by Navajo silversmiths, back in the 1870's.

Uncle started sketching a design for a ketoh. Slim Runner asked permission to try making a design. He picked up a piece of paper and soon had drawn several variations of Uncle's old ketoh. Slim Runner did not especially like the stone on the old ketoh, and so he left it out of the designs. Uncle was very pleased with the designs and decided to make the ketohs without stones. This would make them less expensive.

Slim Runner had enjoyed sketching designs for ketohs, and he was happy when Uncle suggested that he sketch designs for other pieces of jewelry. "This is almost as interesting as making designs for paintings," he said to himself.

Uncle then taught Slim Runner how to carve the molds for ketohs. After the molds were made, the pouring, filing, dipping into nitric acid, and polishing of the ketohs took several days. Slim Runner was allowed to solder copper loops to the underside of each ketoh, while Uncle cut a wide leather band as a backing for the ketoh. After the leather band was attached, they made holes along the edges of it, and laced narrow leather strips through them. To put a ketoh on, a man simply loosened the thongs, slipped the ketoh on his wrist, and tightened the lacing to fit.

Slim Runner finished cleaning up. As usual,

he carefully brushed the silver filings into a can and was ready for more work. Uncle needed a chain for the pendant he had made earlier that week. He took a pair of long-nosed pliers and showed Slim Runner how to twist silver wire into a chain. At last the boy was working with silver.

About a week later, they wrapped the three ketohs in an old piece of cloth. Uncle wore the pendant, which hung from the silver chain Slim Runner had made. As they drove to the trading post, they discussed the tools Uncle was planning to buy for Slim Runner. They reached the trading post and went in to sell the finished silver. Everyone crowded around the counter to admire the new designs and the workmanship. The trader shook hands with Uncle and Slim Runner, and praised them for having done so much work.

"It is different now," Uncle said proudly. "I have a helper, my nephew here. I'm supposed to teach him to work in silver. But sometimes I don't know whether I'm teaching him or learning from him. We are really partners." Then Uncle took the money from the trader and gave half of it to Slim Runner.

Slim Runner was too embarrassed to look at Uncle. He looked instead at the glass case where Navajo jewelry was displayed for sale. He noted with pride that the pieces Uncle and he had made really stood out. He put the money Uncle gave him into his pocket and moved over to the grocery counter to buy food for Mother's hogan.

When Slim Runner returned to his family at the end of the summer, they had good news for him. Older Brother would be finished with school in another year and would come home to help with the sheep again. That meant that Slim Runner could go to art school then.

The boy felt very happy. He had reached his goals. He had grown to enjoy working in silver, and he could earn money for his parents in the summertime. And now he would be able to study painting, too. Perhaps he would be a great painter someday. But meanwhile, he was content to be a good silversmith.

6

THE NAVAJO TODAY

The Navajo came to the Southwest after the
expedition of the Spanish explorer Coronado
in 1540. Together with the Apache, they came
as hunters in search of game. For the first
time they saw pueblos, lying along the Rio
Grande, to the south and west. The people in
these pueblos were farmers, who spent the
spring and long, hot summer tending their
small patches of corn, beans, and squash, and
raised enough to last from harvest to harvest.
This, together with hunting rabbits and wild
fowl, and gathering wild plants, herbs, and
berries, enabled these people to live securely.

The Navajo and Apache wanderers coming
down from the north thought these pueblos
very desirable. They formed raiding parties

that would swoop down at dawn on an unsuspecting pueblo after its men had left for the fields. They took everything in sight—not only the corn, the strings of dried squash, and the basketfuls of beans, but also the women and children.

As the years went by, the Navajo raiders discovered the usefulness of sheep. They had accumulated flocks of them by raiding settlement after settlement. In time the Navajo became excellent sheepherders. There was ample pasturage in the grassy northern part of the Southwest, where the Navajo now roamed. They liked to eat mutton. They used sheepskins to keep warm in winter, and were learning from the Pueblos how to shear the sheep, card, spin, and weave blankets. After a while the warm blankets that the Navajo women had learned to make became so popular that they could not weave them fast enough to supply the demand.

As their flocks and population increased, the

Navajo pushed westward. They moved on to a wide, flat land dotted with mesas. To the south were meadows with springs and trees. These were good grazing lands. The early Navajo built their earth-covered houses here, and laid claim to grazing territories.

By the time an American army had come to the Southwest in 1846, the Navajo were a rich people. Some raiding still continued, but it was done more for excitement than for plunder. They had large flocks of sheep, herds of horses, mules, and cattle. They had permanent dwellings—the hogans—and ample pasture for their flocks. The country was still lush with grass. The men had small patches of corn which they tended halfheartedly, because, unlike the Pueblo men, they liked to move about the country. Parties of men roamed the plains and hunted deer and buffalo. This period, just before the Americans came, was really the best for the Navajo.

New Mexico became a Territory in 1850,

and the United States Army moved in to stay. The white settlers' first complaints to the Army were about the Navajo and Apache raiders. The Army ruled that there should be no more raids, and invited all the Indians to a council to sign a peace treaty. Almost every group from the Southwest was represented: the Pueblo Indians of the Rio Grande, the Hopi, the Zuni, and the independent, roving Apache bands; but the Navajo did not come.

The Government decided to send Captain Reid, with thirty volunteers, to meet the Navajo in their own domain and talk with them. A Navajo chief named Sandoval led Reid and his men into Navajo country. Sandoval belonged to a small group of Navajo who had adopted Christianity and were friendly toward the white men. He took them to an old and rich Navajo, Narbona. Because young Navajo warriors often raided Narbona's extensive flocks, he was willing to help Reid. He sent out his sheep-herders to gather together as many Navajo as possible. Reid and his men waited for several days. Then the Navajo horsemen began to arrive in thousands. They agreed to select chiefs from among themselves and to send them to talk peace with the new conquerors.

The meeting took place at Bear Water, where the white men had built a fort called Fort Wingate. The Navajo resented this fort. The land upon which it had been built belonged to them, and there was a fresh-water spring there. Water is scarce in that part of the country; yet the white men kept the Navajo from using the water and paid them nothing for it.

The five hundred Navajo representatives met to talk of peace. The white man's peace had to be explained to the Navajo, whose logic was not white men's logic. "Why should we stop raiding? You continue your wars," said one of the Navajo chiefs.

After much discussion, the terms of the

treaty were read to them. They were to remain within the boundaries of their four sacred
mountains, and they were to stop their raids.
The Navajo had agreed, when one of the white
men suddenly discovered that a Navajo chief
was riding a horse that had been stolen from
him a while back. He spoke of this to the
colonel, who ordered the Navajo to give up
the horse. The Navajo patiently explained that
he had not stolen it. The horse had been traded
to him by a friend, who had obtained it from
another man, who had probably got it from
still another man.

"Seize the horse!" the colonel commanded.
The Navajo chiefs jumped on their horses
and galloped away. A guard fired several shots.
He killed one horseman, eighty-year-old Narbona. Six other Navajo were wounded and
died of these wounds later.

After that, it was no use talking peace to
the outraged Navajo. They started their raids

anew, determined to avenge their dead. The white soldiers, in retaliation, burned Navajo cornfields and homes.

With the coming of the Civil War, 1861-1865, the Army's attention turned elsewhere. Troops withdrew from the Southwest. The Navajo took advantage of this and intensified their raiding. The Confederate Army invaded the Southwest for a while, but failed to conquer it and so withdrew. A Union army of 1500 men was stationed there after the Confederate withdrawal. General James Henry Carleton, in charge of the Union soldiers, set them to work repairing the damaged countryside. The men grumbled. They had come there to fight a war, not to repair fences, houses, and roads.

Encouraged by Governor Henry Connelly of Sante Fe, General Carleton decided to use his man power to rid New Mexico of Apache and Navajo. He consulted with Colonel Christopher Carson, known as Kit Carson, and asked him to lead an expedition. Kit Carson at first refused to fight the Indians, because he believed that they could be brought to terms without a war. But General Carleton's men wanted to fight, and so he finally agreed to help them.

A ruthless removal of the Apache and Navajo began. In a proclamation in 1863, Carleton said that the Navajo Indians had robbed and murdered the people of New Mexico. He said that this must be stopped and the Navajo must be punished. When Kit Carson moved against the Navajo, he hired a band of Utes to help fight them. The Utes had been enemies of the Navajo for a long time. Within a week they reported that they had killed eight Navajo men and captured four women and seven children. Carson and Carleton favored turning over these captives to the white settlers as slaves, but the War Department did not permit this. Thereafter, women and children were slaughtered along with the men.

Actually, the Navajo were in no position to

take a stand against the white men. They did not have enough of a surplus of corn or wheat to keep them supplied with food during a war. Though they owned thousands of horses, these were good only for quick, short trips and were no match for the white man's cavalry. Furthermore, the Navajo had practically no guns or ammunition. It was not their custom to organize under a central chief, so they could not unite against the white invaders. But still they continued to resist the army.

Carleton began to formulate a plan for resettling the Navajo in a smaller territory, where they could more easily be kept under control. He made several trips in search of such a place, and finally settled on Bosque Redondo—an area some forty square miles around Fort Sumner, on the Pecos River in New Mexico. The rolling plains seemed ideal for grazing, and the Pecos River seemed good for irrigating tracts of land for farming. The General did not know that the land was sandy and poor, and could not support more than 200 people. He planned to move 7000 Navajo there.

General Carleton was anxious to put his plan into action. He kept writing letters to his officers in the field, urging them to round up the Navajo for this mass migration. The orders finally boiled down to this: either bring the Navajo to Bosque Redondo or kill them.

In January 1864, Kit Carson came to Canyon de Chelly (Shay), then the heart of the Navajo country. He killed twenty-three Navajo and took thirty-four prisoners. On the following morning, hundreds of women and children began to surrender. Dressed in rags, clutching thin, half-starved babies, the women begged the soldiers not to kill their children. They said that many Navajo had already died of starvation. Soon the men began to surrender too.

Kit Carson's soldiers celebrated the victory by setting fire to the beautiful peach orchards on the bottom of the canyon. The Navajo could not believe that the white conquerors would actually do this to them. As the first tongue of fire leaped up, the Navajo men went crazy with anger. With the little strength they had left, they hurled themselves upon the soldiers, trying to save the precious peach trees that had taken so many years to grow.

Three months later, 2400 Navajo started the long trip to Bosque Redondo. It was a sad procession. Frightened men, women, and children, lined up in two's and four's, marched silently across the Puerco River, then across the Rio Grande to Albuquerque. From Albuquerque they traveled eastward over the mountains, toward Fort Sumner.

By 1866 Carleton had collected almost 7000 Navajo at Bosque Redondo. An estimated thousand Navajo were still at large.

Carleton was having trouble feeding and clothing the captives. All goods had to be brought in from the east, through a country full of train robbers and outlaws. The people lived on a starvation diet; and many sickened with pneumonia, smallpox, and other white men's diseases. The Navajo died by the hundreds. To add to these troubles, the crops all over the Southwest failed in 1865. A combination of early frosts, drought, and insects had destroyed them. The Navajo had worked hard on their small cornfields at Bosque Redondo, but had harvested nothing.

The citizens of New Mexico began protesting to Washington over the Navajo plight. So did the Indian agents, appointed by the Bureau of Indian Affairs and sent to New Mexico to work with the Indians. On September 19, 1866, General Carleton was at last removed. Congress passed an act in 1868 authorizing treaty making with the Indians. General William Tecumseh Sherman and Colonel Samuel F. Tappan reached Fort Sumner on May 28, 1868. Within three days they had drawn up a treaty with the Navajo. It was accepted by both the government and the Navajo, and at long last the captives were released to return home.

In the treaty the government agreed to give the Navajo $150,000 for rehabilitation, to provide transportation back home, and to furnish 15,000 sheep and goats and 500 head of cattle to rebuild their livestock. Every Navajo was to receive an annual token payment of five dollars. Farmers and craftsmen were to receive ten dollars annually. Heads of families were promised land and seeds and farm implements, valued up to one hundred dollars for the first year, and twenty-five dollars for the two succeeding years. In turn, the Navajo promised to send their children——between the ages of six and thirteen——to school. The government promised to provide a teacher and schoolhouse for every thirty children.

On June 15, 1868, the few thousand remaining Navajo began the trek back to their homelands. Four companies of United States cavalry were there to prevent any fighting. But the escort was hardly necessary. The Navajo were going home, and they were not going to

give the white men an excuse to stop them. Traveling a little over ten miles a day, with more than a hundred wagons and some five thousand head of cattle, they covered the distance from Bosque Redondo to Albuquerque in about twenty-one days. The Navajo were still about a hundred and fifty miles east of their own country, but they could see its mountains and mesas. Many of the men went wild with excitement. To keep from running ahead, they asked to be tied to the wagons.

At last they were back home again. As group after group went off to the lands that had belonged to them, they found their old homes in ruins. They had been burned by soldiers, or uprooted by winds and storms. The slow, painful process of reconstruction began.

Almost a century has since passed. The Navajo are still mainly sheepherders, weavers, and silversmiths; but great changes are now taking place in Navajo country. These changes have already affected hundreds of Navajo families. The over-all effects are yet to be seen. But the future looks bright for the Navajo.

In less than a century the Navajo population has grown from the few thousand that had returned from Bosque Redondo in 1868, to almost eighty-five thousand today. But since no more land was allotted to them, the majority of Navajo remained very poor. However, a turn for the better began in 1950.

A Navajo who had mined vanadium, which is a mineral used in toughening steel, became curious when he saw white men with Geiger counters wandering around the mountains of Arizona in search of uranium. In 1950, he bought a Geiger counter too, and set out for the Lukachukai Mountains. For quite a while the counter, or "the-box-that-talks," remained silent. But one day, as the Navajo miner faced a high canyon wall, the box began to chatter. There in the Morrison Salt Wash was the yellow uranium ore. He laid out his stake. Ar-

rangements were made for the Walter Duncan
Mining Company to lease and operate the new
mine, called the Cisco Mine. Its discoverer
would receive royalties for the ore mined. With
the money he received, the Navajo improved
his farm, built a nicer home for his family, and
bought a pickup truck.

The news of this find spread among other
Navajo who had mined vanadium. Some
bought Geiger counters and set off for the
Lukachukai Mountains. Another Navajo found
uranium in a canyon wall, directly opposite the
Cisco Mine. This mine is also very productive.

Several other uranium deposits were found
in the northwestern Lukachukai Range; and
the search spread into Monument Valley, where
today the mine called Monument #2 is one
of the biggest in the country.

The Navajo Tribal Council has been keeping
watch over the distribution of the income from
these mines and from the oil and natural gas
developments on the reservation. The Tribal

Council consists of seventy-four members, selected by the entire Navajo population. They meet every three months at the Navajo capitol, Window Rock, Arizona. Their meetings are not unlike our own state congressional meetings, although the Navajo still prefer to have their decisions unanimous, as they did in the old days.

In 1950 Congress authorized an appropriation of $88,500,000 for the rehabilitation of the Navajo and Hopi Indians. The rehabilitation is directed toward improvements in irrigation and land management, and toward the better use of timber and minerals. In addition, the Tribal Council is using some of this money to bring small industries to Navajo country. Because of the excellent manual dexterity of the Navajo, they are exceptionally good at assembling small metal parts; and several such industries, scattered throughout their land, would give greater financial security to the people.

WINDOW ROCK

In 1956 the Tribal Council faced their biggest and perhaps their most welcome problem. Toward the end of that year, the Navajo Tribal treasury was to receive several million dollars from the oil, gas, and uranium and vanadium mines. It was important to work out a fair distribution of these funds, so that the Navajo would get the most benefit from them in the present, as well as in the future. Schools and hospitals headed the list, and are still of prime importance in the Council's allotment of funds.

In 1956 school enrollment reached a peak of 25,000. This does not mean that all Navajo children are going to school today. Many families still have to decide which of their children can be spared from the pressing work of the household and sheepherding, just as the family of Slim Runner had to do. To make education compulsory for every child is the Tribal Council's aim today. It will take time, however, to accomplish this among a population so spread out, with the obstacles of poor roads and poor communication.

The Navajo also clamor for more hospitals. As yet there are not enough hospitals to take care of all their needs. It is hoped that in time there will be enough—with perhaps more trained Navajo nurses and even Navajo doctors.

Although hundreds of Navajo today work in the mines, earning good pay, many still have to look for work outside Navajo country. They find work in the surrounding towns, but at best only a few jobs are open to them. The women work as maids or waitresses, and the men work as mechanics. The Indian Bureau encourages these men and women to learn to live away from their reservation, and tries to help them out financially to some extent. Some of these people have succeeded. Others have not, and have returned to the reservation, disappointed and dissatisfied. These Navajo need help in getting adjusted.

Only a short while ago, the Navajo were a

poverty-stricken people—almost without hope. But the recent turn of events has helped them regain their pride and their hope for a better future. May their paths be full of beauty, health, and happiness!

INDEX

*Indicates illustrations

157